PUFFIN BOOKS

SLAPSTICK

For over forty years Roger McGough has been one of the leading lights of British poetry for children and adults alike. In 2001 he was given the Freedom of the City of Liverpool, and in 2004 he was awarded the CBE for services to literature.

THE WOW!

If Philosophy is the Why?
and Science the How?
then Poetry is the Wow!

ROGER McGOUGH

SLAPSTICK

POEMS

ILLUSTRATED BY
ADAM STOWER

PUFFIN

For Bobby and Lola McGough

PUFFIN BOOKS

Published by the Penguin Group
Penguin Books Ltd, 80 Strand, London WC2R 0RL, England
Penguin Group (USA) Inc., 375 Hudson Street, New York, New York 10014, USA
Penguin Group (Canada), 90 Eglinton Avenue East, Suite 700, Toronto, Ontario, Canada M4P 2Y3
(a division of Pearson Penguin Canada Inc.)
Penguin Ireland, 25 St Stephen's Green, Dublin 2, Ireland (a division of Penguin Books Ltd)
Penguin Group (Australia), 250 Camberwell Road, Camberwell, Victoria 3124, Australia
(a division of Pearson Australia Group Pty Ltd)
Penguin Books India Pvt Ltd, 11 Community Centre, Panchsheel Park, New Delhi – 110 017, India
Penguin Group (NZ), 67 Apollo Drive, Rosedale, North Shore 0632, New Zealand
(a division of Pearson New Zealand Ltd)
Penguin Books (South Africa) (Pty) Ltd, 24 Sturdee Avenue, Rosebank, Johannesburg 2196, South Africa

Penguin Books Ltd, Registered Offices: 80 Strand, London WC2R 0RL, England

puffinbooks.com

First published 2008
1

Text copyright © Roger McGough, 2008
Illustrations copyright © Adam Stower, 2008
All rights reserved

The moral right of the author and illustrator has been asserted

Set in Sabon
Made and printed in England by Clays Ltd, St Ives plc

British Library Cataloguing in Publication Data
A CIP catalogue record for this book is available from the British Library

ISBN: 978–0–141–32507–1

www.greenpenguin.co.uk

Penguin Books is committed to a sustainable future
for our business, our readers and our planet.
The book in your hands is made from paper
certified by the Forest Stewardship Council.

ACKNOWLEDGEMENTS

A version of 'Lily the Pink', arranged and sung by The Scaffold, was a number one hit in 1968.

'Mummy Won't Be Home for Christmas', recorded by The Scaffold, was not a number one hit in 1974.

'Tsunami' was first published as 'All in Time to the Music' in *Lucky* in 1993.

CONTENTS

DON'T LAUGH AT ME
COS I'M A STICK INSECT

I may be a stick insect
but I'm not thin
I'm thick

I married my childhood sweetheart
who turned out to be
a stick.

1

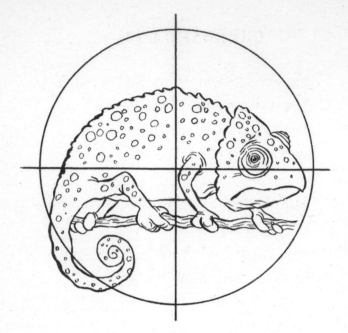

MEALS ON LEAVES

Chameleons
who are colour-blind
are hopeless
at camouflage

Red and green
they look the same
so by and large
they're easy game.

CUPBOARD LOVE

Said the cockroach to the henroach
'To this cupboard are you new?
Such a carapace, capacious,
curvacious, blacky-blue.

I think of polished leather
and my heart I give to you
Let us make our home together
In a lady's dancing shoe.'

FRUIT BATS

Fruit bats come in all shapes and sizes
banana-shaped
pear-shaped
they're full of surprises

Hanging in the belfry
is that a satsuma?
Another example
of crazy bats' humour?

You think that's a strawberry
glowing on a bush?
You go to pick it and *whoosh*
What a fright!

As arrowing, shrieking
it takes flight
into the deaf, eternal
black bat night.

TENUOUS LINKS

Consider the lynx
A joker, a jinx

In America a lynx is a bobcat
In Poland a pigeon (that's true)

So pity the lynx
Who everyday thinks

Am I the hunter or am I the prey
Do I pounce or fly away?

RUDE KANGAROO

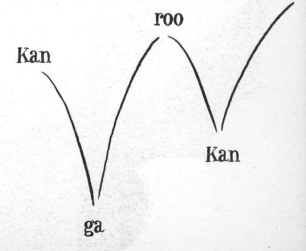

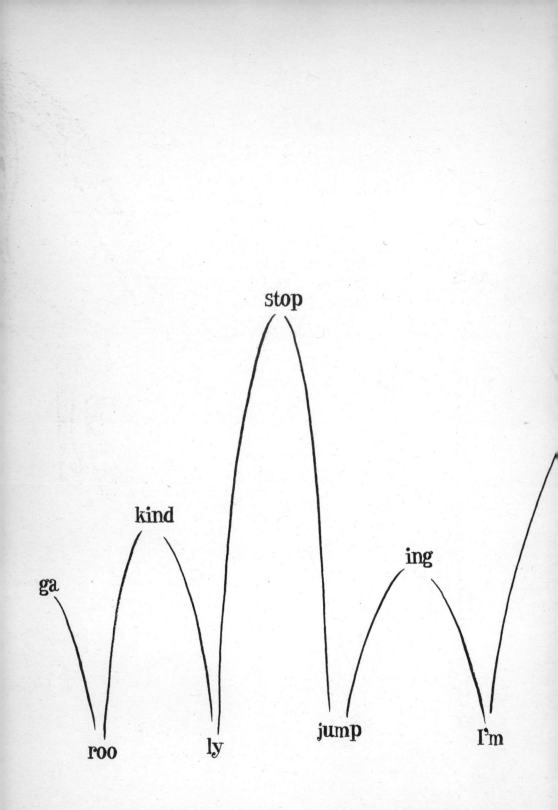

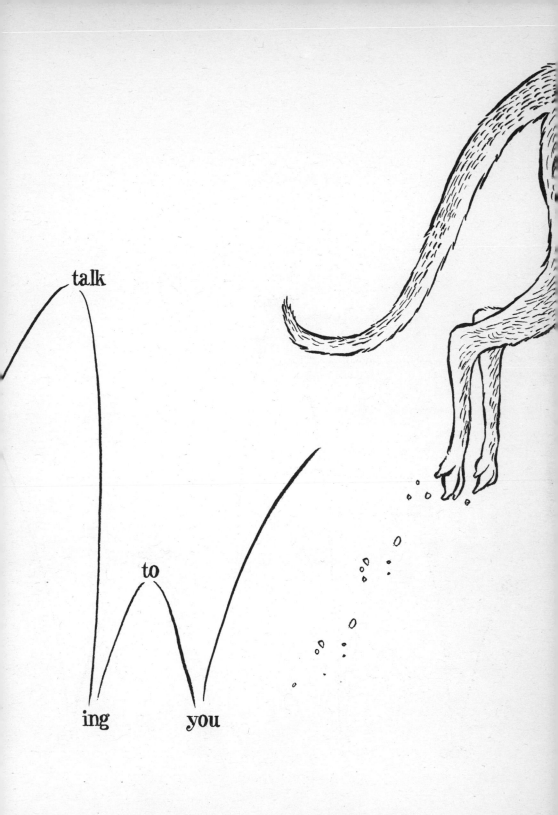

DUMB GIRAFFE

travelled
lungs has
from the
expelled
the air
by the time
to speak,
it decides
whenever
because
Or is it
choice?
through
is it
voice,
gives
never
giraffe
that a
The fact

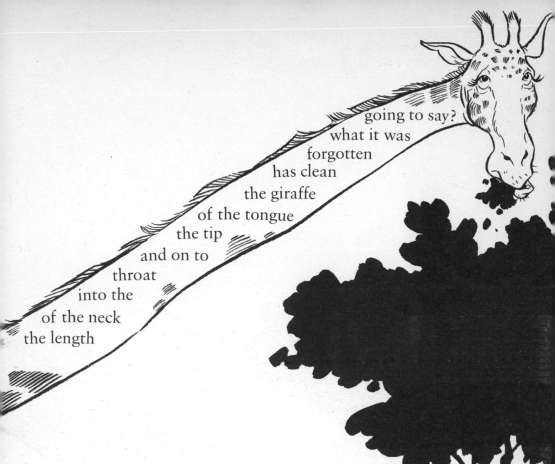

going to say?
what it was
forgotten
has clean
the giraffe
of the tongue
the tip
and on to
throat
into the
of the neck
the length

PUFF

Ever see baboons
Playing with balloons?

They haven't got the puff
To blow them up enough.

GORILLA LOVE

Sometimes
as a special treat
she'll peel me a banana
with her feet

Rid my back
of all its fleas
then run and hide
among the trees

With excitement
I grow weaker
I count to ten
and forget to seek her.

THE TOFU-EATING TIGER

If a tiger invites you round for tea
and offers you tofu,
you can take it from me
he's only pretending.

It's merely a ploy
to fool an innocent girl or boy
into thinking he's sweet.
A vegetarian tiger who doesn't eat meat.

Rubbish! Just look at those jaws.
Were they designed for chewing rice?
And those claws. For peeling bananas?
Take my advice:

Stay calm. Be polite.
Eat up your tofu and ask for more.
When the feline is in the kitchen
make a beeline for the door.

THE FEATHER BOA CONSTRICTOR

The feather boa constrictor
It's no joke

It tickles as it tightens

You burst out laughing
Then you choke.

NAUGHTY CATERPILLAR

There's a caterpillar
crawling on my cheek
and it tickles

Now it's hugging
my left eyebrow
and it prickles

I'm sure she would kiss it
if I let her
The sooner the butterfly

the better!

CROCODILE WARNINGS

Be careful, there is a crocodile crossing the road

You mean a zebra crossing

Do zebras chew lollipopmen?

* * *

Be careful, there is a crocodile marching along the pavement

Of children?

For children

* * *

Be careful, there is a crocodile in the gutter

That's only a puddle

Do puddles have interlocking teeth?

Jigsaw puddles do.

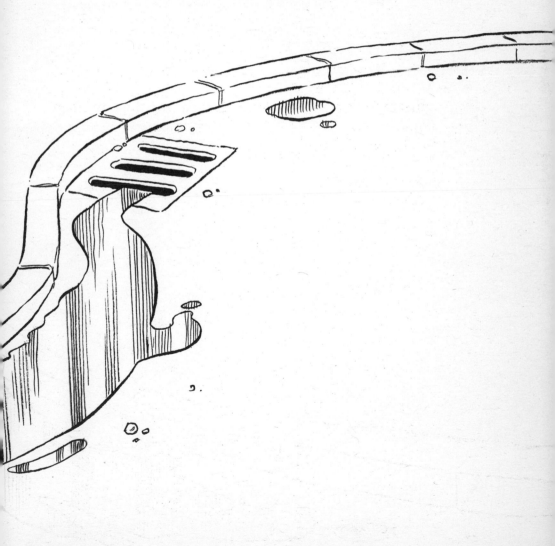

CROAK

Frog can't croak
Frog can't croak
Got a man in his throat
It's no joke

NEVER GOAD A TOAD

Never goad a toad
or call him names

He won gold
in sumo wrestling
at the Amphibious Games.

CANE TOADS?

Please don't.

Even when they're naughty
and you think they deserve it

A good telling off
will usually suffice

Corporal punishment
is not very nice.

GINGER

Goldfish are not cold fish
Mine's a friendly little chap

After a few lengths of the bowl
He likes to curl up on my lap

A quiet snooze then time for his feed
So I polish his scales and put on his lead

We stroll into town as people stare
At a goldfish enjoying the morning air

We settle into our local pub
Where Ginger tucks into his favourite grub

Battered cod with chips galore
Then half a lager through a straw

We dawdle home to watch TV
My pet beside me on the settee
I bet you wish you had a fish like me.

JELLYFISH MORTON

This morning,
out walking, I saw
a jellyfish playing piano
on the shore

The hottest jazz
the coolest blues
I started to dance
in my shiny shoes

'What's your name?'
I asked
when he stopped for tea

'Jellyfish Morton,'
he said
'and you can take it from me

It don't mean a thing
if it ain't got sting.'
Then he slipped back into the sea.

HOOVER, THE TALKING SEAL*

An audacious, loquacious seal
called Hoover, after each meal,
having vacuumed the fish
straight out of the dish
would jabber and babble
blabber and gabble
chatter and prattle
and spiel.

* An aquarium in New England is where Hoover the famous talking seal lived
  until his death in 1985. Not a great conversationalist, his repertoire consisted
  only of 'How are ya' and 'Get outta here'. But not bad for a seal.

WHALE IN THE THAMES

Didn't see it in the flesh
     though thousands did

Read all the coverage
     in the papers

Watched the drama unfold
     on television

Sad she didn't make it
     to the open sea

Would have made
     a really nice ending.

WORDS ON A RIVER

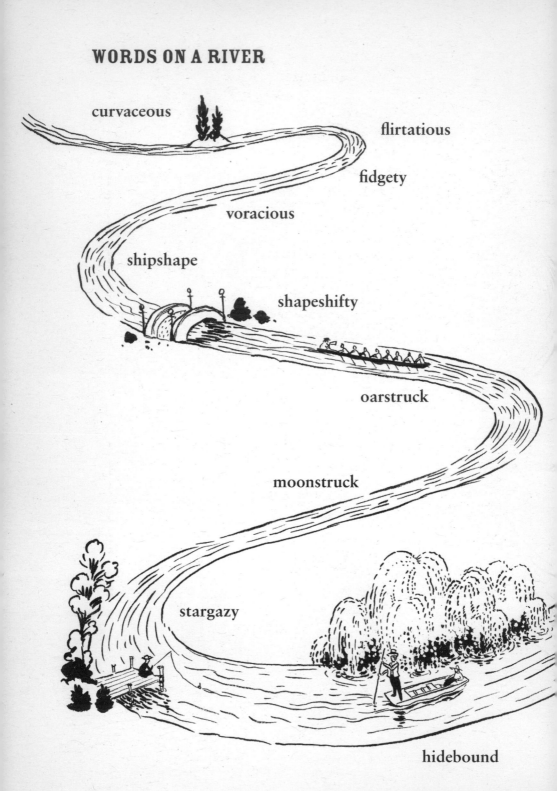

curvaceous

flirtatious

fidgety

voracious

shipshape

shapeshifty

oarstruck

moonstruck

stargazy

hidebound

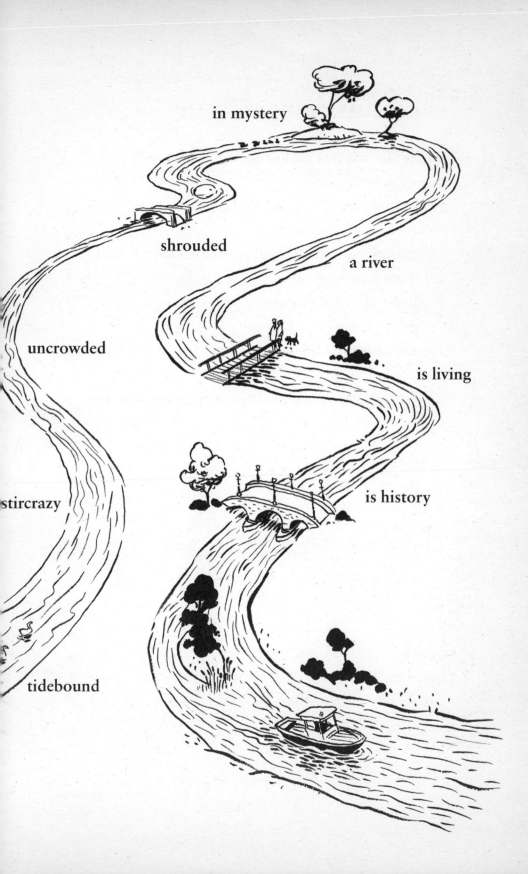

in mystery

shrouded

a river

uncrowded

is living

stircrazy

is history

tidebound

THE COBBLE BOAT

When she helped rescue four men and a woman
from the wreck of the *Melrose* in September 1832
Amy at nineteen, became a national hero.

Queen Victoria wrote in person to thank her
The Poet Laureate penned verses in her honour
Impresarios invited her to appear on stage.

But she would not be tempted by wealth or fame
and when my wife died, Amy took her place
helping me run the lighthouse on Strachan Isle.

* * *

When the paddle steamer *Durness* hit Ravens Rock
on the ninth of November 1835, it was my daughter,
on watch in the lantern gallery, who raised the alarm.

There being no time to alert the lifeboat station,
we launched the cobble boat and rowed out
to the wreck. Sadly, there were no survivors.

It was shortly after midnight two months later
that the SS *Kinsale* carrying a cargo of cloths from Hull
to Dundee went aground on the same accursed rocks.

Again, I was asleep while Amy was upstairs tending
the lamp. Again, we rowed out in the same frail, open boat,
and again the sea was as smooth as a raven's wing.

* * *

And many a night thereafter, I was haunted by the screams
of the poor souls hauled from the reef, and the dying words
of the young midshipman: 'The light. Where is the light?'

For I feared it was not the shadow of death of which
he spoke. And with the loss of another ship soon after,
I took action before an investigation could begin.

My eldest son joined me on Strachan Isle, and I sent
Amy back to the mainland in the care of her sister Martha,
with strict orders to confine her to the house.

I cannot blame Martha for what happened
on that night of the worst gale in living memory
for Amy was possessed by a demonic force.

Drawn by the siren calls for help she escaped
and guided by the lighthouse beam rowed towards
the ghostly hulk broken on the back of Ravens Rock.

Next morning, when the storm subsided, we found
no sign of a shipwreck, nor of Amy. Only the splintered
remains of a cobble boat washed up on the shore.

GATEWAY TO THE ATLANTIC

I am the warm hello and the sad farewell

I am the path to glory and the road to hell

I am the gull on the wing and the salt in the air

I am the night patrol and the morning prayer

I am the port register, read the names with pride

I am the thickening fog and the quickening tide

I am the ferryboat, the slaver, the man-o'-war

I am the keeper of the quays, welcome ashore

I am the starstruck, eternal romantic

I am the gateway to the Atlantic.

RIDDLE

You'll find me on hairy forearms and oiled biceps
Rose-tinted imitations of the real thing.
Black-browed and hard as nails, that's me

I'll come down on you like a ton of bricks
So I'm kept in chains though there's nowhere to run.
Bottom-scraper, bed-impaler, call me what you like,

I'll sling my hook when it's time to call it a day
And while you're still stuck in the mud
I'm aweigh.

THE PERFECT SHAPE

Not drops of water
frozen into the perfect shape
of a snowflake

But snowflakes
tossed into the air
and falling to earth

Frozen
into the perfect shape
of a snowman.

WELCOME, WINTER

Winter's here, no doubt about it
and though there's many could do without it
I say, welcome.

Welcome, for summer's tired, it needs a rest.
We hardly noticed autumn, at best
it was a dying fall.

Welcome, cooling winds and snow
replenish the earth, make things grow
watering-can in hand.

Welcome, twilight in the afternoon
that early glimpse of star and moon
fresh and inquisitive.

Welcome, fog and swirling mist
mysterious, you get the gist,
haloed lights and muffled footsteps.

Welcome, hot drinks and warm coats
aching limbs, sore throats
and headaches, Oh dear.

A bout of flu, no doubt about it
I blame the weather, could do without it.
So dull and drab and dreary.

Writing this has made me weary
I dream of summer and feel cheery.
Winter, you've outstayed your welcome.

JACK FROST

Look out!
There's a joker about
waiting for you to step
on that sheet of ice

Then *whoosh!*
he pulls it out
from under your feet
and down you go

On your bum in the snow
Ow!

MUMMY WON'T BE HOME FOR CHRISTMAS

Mummy won't be home for Christmas
Hear the distant church bells ring
Peace on earth, goodwill to men
To us kids don't mean a thing

Mummy went away in October
Daddy says she won't be back
Snow is falling thick all over
Christmas sure is looking black

Mummy's living in Southampton
Daddy says she's happier there
But I don't think she'd desert us
If she knew how much we care

We've put up the decorations
We've hung tinsel everywhere
But the tree looks kinda lonely
Seems to know that she's not there

Santa brought us extra presents
Daddy must have told him so
But they lie there still unopened
Us kids don't want to know

The cake was bought on eBay
There are Morrisons mince pies
But it's not like her home cooking
There are tears in Daddy's eyes

Now it's time for Christmas Dinner
And Daddy says, just in case
Before we say thanksgiving
We'll set Mummy's usual place

Into the silence of our eating came a footstep on the stair
Daddy took off his paper hat and mouthed a silent prayer
The door was slowly opened, the moonlight in her hair
Like a vision, pure and lovely, Mummy was standing there

Mummy's come home for Christmas
Everything has turned out right
Mummy's come home for Christmas
Now our Christmas will be white

Mummy's come home for Christmas
And she says she's gonna stay
Now we all agree with Daddy
It's our happiest Christmas Day.

ON THE THIRTEENTH
DAY OF CHRISTMAS
MY TRUE LOVE SENT
TO ME ... A TEXT

Drummers n pipers
n car park a-fightin
Lrds wen nt
milkmaids a-kissin
Hens, geese, swans
n turtle doves a-shootin
5 gld rings
n partridge a-missin
cnt gt in2 Ladies 4 ladies
bt hope 2 B nxt n
wl set fyr 2 pear trE
wen finshd a-textin
thx a bunch
yr ex-true luv
(p.s. mrry Txtmas)

OVID

(A BOUSTROPHEDON*)

One morning Ovid hitched his oxen to the plough
Rome near fields father's his in work to set and
The sun beat down upon him but unaware of the intense
dreams and hexameters with filled was head his heat
of Daphne Diana Narcissus Echo and Apollo
Myrrah and Actaeon Crocale Cupid Venus of
And the lines that he composed unlike the furrows
imagination world's the in on live soil Apennine the in

* A Greek word meaning 'as the ox turns in ploughing'.
Read from left to right, then head back in the opposite direction.

HOW TO START A POEM

Knowing how to start a poem
is easier than knowing how to
start a poem is easier than knowing
how to start a poem is easier

than knowing how to start
a poem is easier than knowing
how to start a poem is easier
than knowing how to start

a poem is easier than knowing
how to start a poem is easier
than knowing how to start
a poem is easier than knowing

how to start a poem is easier
than knowing how to start
a poem is easier than knowing
how to start a poem. The end.

HOW TO END A POEM

Knowing how to end a poem
is not as easy as people think.
It's not simply a matter
of putting in a full stop
and then adding your name.

My advice would be to count up to ten
and then shout, 'One more line
and then I'm coming, ready or not.'

WHAT'S UP, POEM

Why is it
    that as soon
        as a poem
            starts to get
                interesting

it stops?

STRAIGHT TALK

I prevaricate
You tell it like it is
I fabricate
You lay it all down

I beat about the bush
You go straight to the heart
I spin a web, fantasize
You speak clearly, analyse

I um and ah, procrastinate
You simplify, illuminate
All smoke and mirrors, I obfuscate
You clear the decks, communicate

I am a dreamer
You are a doer
Let's get together.

WORDS

Like birds
who dream of eggs
before laying them

Words
I try to weigh
before saying them.

PLAY-ACTING

The curtain is rising
Light fills the page

Writing is acting
Without going onstage.

LONELY MONOLOGUE

Than be a lonely monologue
I'd rather be a dialogue
A heartfelt conversation
That two of us can play

Than be a lengthy diatribe
I'd rather be a heart-to-heart
Where I can listen patiently
Before I have my say

Than be a rabble-rousing speech
I'd rather be a quiet aside
A word in your ear,
For if truth be said
Than be a voice in the wilderness
I'd rather be a head-to-head.

ALL THE WORLD'S A SOAP

All the world's a soap and all the men and women merely extras,
bit players who drift in and out of the action,
feeding you lines to move the story forward.
For you are the star.

As a baby in the opening episode,
cooing in the Lady-Who-Plays-Your-Mother's arms,
your first words brought the house down.
Your first steps had us on the edge of our seats.

'A million billion willion miles from home
waiting for the bell to go . . .' A child's
first day at school, you captured perfectly
that mix of nervousness and wondrous anticipation.

The awkward charm and vulnerability you brought
to the role of a teenager in episode three
never lapsed into vulgar parody,
and will be talked of long after transmission.

As a twenty-something you were so cool and sexy,
some of the cast were jealous. But you brought
humour to the part, and everyone was delighted
when eventually you fell in love and settled down.

In the fifth episode, the anxious parent
moving reluctantly towards middle age
with a sense of time rushing by. The role
might have been written for you. In fact it was.

'It's a joy to be old, kids through school,
the dog dead and the car sold.' In number six
as a senior citizen, you made sense of old age,
playing the part with dignity and warmth.

The last episode brought tears to everybody's eyes.
Lying in the One-Who-Plays-Your-Lover's arms
your dying words inspired a sense of hope
As the final credits rolled on *All the World's a Soap*.

LILY THE PINK

We'll drink, a drink, a drink
To Lily the Pink, the Pink, the Pink
The saviour of the human race
For she invented medicinal compound
Most efficacious in every case

Lily the Pink invented a drink
(Some people say she was a witch)
It tasted strong, had a terrible pong
But it made her incredibly rich

Born in Alaska, she moved to Nebraska
In the wild and woolly west
From a medicine man bought a pink caravan
So in pink, she always dressed

The sheriff of Tulsa had a terrible ulcer
Wind blew him up like a balloon
So they gave him medicinal compound
Now he's floating round the moon

We'll drink, a drink, a drink
To Lily the Pink, the Pink, the Pink
The saviour of the human race
For she invented medicinal compound
Most efficacious in every case

For Lily's invention, I need hardly mention
Had the weirdest side effects
People swallowed it, happiness followed it
But wait till you hear what happened next

Cousin Eva suffered hay fever
All summer long she'd sneeze and sneeze
When they gave her medicinal compound
She blew the leaves right off the trees

Deputy Fritz had spectacular zits
The spottiest face you'd ever seen
So they gave him medicinal compound
It cleared the spots but turned him green

We'll drink, a drink, a drink
To Lily the Pink, the Pink, the Pink
The saviour of the human race
For she invented medicinal compound
Most efficacious in every case

Mary-Lou Nash had a ginger moustache
Underneath her pretty nose
With application of medication
It grows and grows and grows and grows

Chief Geronimo swallowed a domino
You should have heard his tearful cries
So they gave him medicinal compound
Now he sees spots before his eyes

Chief Sitting Bull was so boring and dull
That his braves refused to pow-wow
Since they gave him medicinal compound
He chases cats and goes bow-wow, wow-wow

We'll drink, a drink, a drink
To Lily the Pink, the Pink, the Pink
The saviour of the human race
For she invented medicinal compound
Most efficacious in every case

Hopalong Cassidy had the sheer audacity
To bring our Lily before the Law
They charged her with false pretences
Then they slammed the jailhouse door

Lily the Pink she turned to drink, she
Filled up with paraffin inside
And despite her medicinal compound
Sadly, pickled Lily died

Up to heaven her soul ascended
All the church bells they did ring
She took with her medicinal compound
Hark, the herald angels sing:

We'll drink, a drink, a drink
To Lily the Pink, the Pink, the Pink
The saviour of the human race
For she invented medicinal compound
Most efficacious in every case.

LOUD ANDY

My friend Andy is a musician.
When not strumming his guitar
or thumping away on the piano
he listens to his CDs, or XFM
played at full volume.

No wonder he has a loud voice.
Even when the two of us
are sitting in a quiet room he shouts
as if competing to be heard
above an imaginary rock band.

Whenever I say
'Andy there's no need to shout,'
he shouts, 'SHOUTING? WHO'S SHOUTING?'

THE SOUL

If eyes
>are the windows of the soul

Are eyelids
>the window cleaners?

LIMERICK

A poet passing through Limerick
Determined to write a fine limerick
He worked day and night
But try as he might
He never got the hang of the limerick.

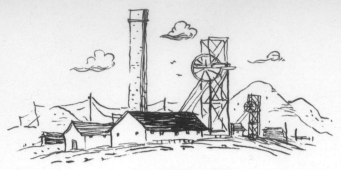

NICKNAMES

Uncle Daffyd was a coal miner
who worked all his life down the mines in Wales
where conditions were terrible and wages low.

To cheer up his workmates, Uncle Daffyd
decided to give them all funny nicknames
and here are just a few of the most hilarious:

A man who was bald he called 'Baldy'
'Strong One' was a man who was strong
'Talk-a-lot' was a miner who talked a lot
And one with bad breath he called 'Pong'.

'Taffy' he nicknamed a Welshman
(and there were hundreds and hundreds of course)
'Big Bottom' a man with a big bottom
And one with a long face he called 'Horse'.

The habit quickly caught on and soon his workmates
had a nickname for Uncle Daffyd. They called him:
'The Not Very Funny Coal miner'.

THEY CALLED ME FOUR EYES . . .

In the playground and in classes
Which was puzzling and cruel
Because I never wore glasses
Until after leaving school.

BAD JOKES

What becomes of jokes that nobody laughs at?

Do they curl up in embarrassment
and wish they'd never been born?
Wish they could bite the tongue
off the one who'd made them?

Do they dread ending up
inside Christmas crackers
or in politicians' speeches?

Like a bellyflop out of water
a joke that nobody laughs at
is a non-slip banana skin.
A custard pie left out in the rain.
An Englishman, an Irishman and a Scotsman
helping a chicken across the road.

Or . . .

Do jokes that nobody laughs at
feel superior? Think the joke is on us
and giggle quietly among themselves?

JOKES

The Racist Joke

I put the boot in
The bully in the pack
Watch out if you're Muslim
Jewish or black.

The Rude Joke

Never properly potty-trained
Always slow to flush
I need to push the limits
Make you squirm, see you blush.

The Hoary Chestnut

I've been around since the caveman
told the knock-knock joke about Dinah . . .
'*Dinah who?*'
'*Dinosaur*'.

OK, it may not seem funny on the page
but it had them falling about in the Stone Age.

The Shaggy Dog Story

I am not so much a joke
as a huge dog, hairy and daft
that jumps up and licks your face
and gobs and slobbers.

And you wish you were in some other place
playing cops and robbers.

But there's no escape
so you have to put up with me
as I wag my tale from breakfast until lunchtime
keeping you waiting for the terrible punchline.

But though I'm unbelievable, long-winded and daft
Go on, admit it, you laughed.

SLAPSTICK

'I'll wipe that smile off your face,'
snarled the teacher, and reaching
into his desk pulled out the wiper.

He dipped the dirty green sponge
into a bucket of disinfectant
and vigorously scrubbed it off.

'Now go back to your place
and I never want to see it again.
Do I make myself clear?'

'Yes, sir.' As I sat down,
the giant wasp I had in mind
flew into the classroom

and stung him on both lips.
He yelped and, stamping
around blindly, put one foot

into the bucket and the other
on top of the smile-wiper
which shot across the so a p y f l o o r t a k i n g

a startled leg with it.

The whole class cheered
when his trousers split
and burst out laughing

when he toppled backwards
over the desk
like a windmill in a hurricane.

But I just smiled.

SLIPSTICK

My sister has started wearing lipstick

Sitting in front of the mirror
she pushes out her lips
as if blowing herself a kiss

Then she slaps it on
Slaps the lipstick on
all over her lips

Slaps the lipstick on
not only her lips
but her chin and her cheeks

Mind you, she's only five
(or will be in two weeks).

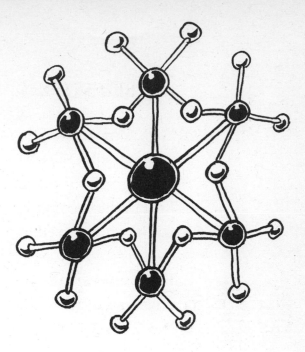

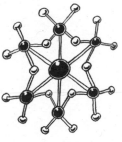

DNA JIGSAW

Not the puzzle
Painstakingly put together

But the pieces
Tossed into the air

And falling to earth
A lifesize picture of you.

INSIDE THE WOMB

I'm Humpty Dumpty
without the wall

Rock-a-bye baby
without the fall

I'm a rubber duck
bouncing
inside a rubber ball.

WHAT DO I DREAM OF?

What do I dream of?
I dream my mother's dreams

I dream my mother
She dreams me

I dream about our past
our future, what it might bring

I hear my mother crying
I hear her sing.

ME

If I were big
　　　I'd want to be sky

If I were little
　　　I'd want to be small elephant

If I were muffin
　　　I'd want to be chocolate

If I were ice cream
　　　I'd want to be strawberry (or chocolate)

If I were drink
　　　I'd want to be fizzy

If I were circus
　　　I'd want to be clown

If I were summer fair
　　　I'd want to be bouncy castle

If I were band
　　　I'd want to be drum

If I were tree
      I'd want to be toffee apple

If I were car
      I'd want to be double-decker bus

If I were water
      I'd want to be sea

If I were someone else
      I'd want to be ME.

HANDS

Touchers and feelers
Holders and hitters
Grippers and graspers
Growers and killers

Open in greeting
Wrung in despair
Clenched in fury
Steepled in prayer.

THE CAT WHO COULDN'T CARE LESS

You've been told to wear braces
You lose your keys
The cat couldn't care less

You trip over your laces
And scrape your knees
The cat just couldn't care less

There's a spot on your nose
Your sock's got a hole in
The cat couldn't care less

The spot grows and grows
Your mobile's been stolen
The cat just couldn't care less

Your ballpoint is leaking
Your jacket is stained
The cat couldn't care less

Your best friend's not speaking
For three days it's rained
The cat just couldn't care less

Mum and Dad fly to Cannes
For a week in the sun
The cat couldn't care less

You go to your gran's
Leave a door latch undone
The cat just couldn't care less

Next day there's a break-in
It goes unreported
The cat couldn't care less

Everything's taken
But there's food and it's watered
So the cat just couldn't care less

The following night
When the squatters drew up
The cat couldn't care less

Set the curtains alight
A gas main blew up
The cat just couldn't care less

Now you stand in the rubble
Give your parents a hug
The cat couldn't care less

Far away from the trouble
Curled up on a rug
The cat just couldn't care less.

SHORT CUT

It happens, doesn't it
when you take a short cut?
You leave the busy road
the tried and trusted route
and take the back way.
The unfamiliar pathway.

And there they are
the gang who seem
to have been expecting you.
Hanging around all day
in the hope you'd happen by.
Without a word, they close in.

You hand it over
Hope they'll let you through.
More often than not, they do.

WHEN NOT TO CUT YOUR NAILS

Cut them on Monday
    It will bring down a curse
Cut them on Tuesday
    Lose your keys and your purse
Cut them on Wednesday
    And you'll follow a hearse
Cut them on Thursday
    It can only get worse
Cut them on Friday
    You'll remember this verse
Cut them on Saturday
    And it's six of the birch
So cut them on Sunday
    (But never in church).

KNITTING NEEDLES

What I find titillating
about knitting needles
is their tittle-tattle.

Spending so much time
locking antlers together
it's a wonder they find
anything new to chat about.

But they do. Pullovers
cardigans, on and on
scarves, thingamabobs
Spinning yarn after yarn after yarn.

Knit one, purl one
birthday surprise.
Pulling the wool
over each other's eyes.

NANA'S KNITTING NEEDLES

Nana's knitting needles
She keeps them in a box
They're neither use nor ornament
I wish she'd knit some socks.

SAFETY PRECAUTION

You bump into a lamp post on the pavement
Your nose it dutifully bleeds

Airbags to wear while out walking
Is what every pedestrian needs.

Platforms are *dangerous*
The line is alive
Fall, and a ghost *train*
May shortly arrive.

SELF-STORAGE

Being unable to control myself
any longer
I travelled by underground
as far as Ongar

Hired a self-storage unit
in a business park
and stored myself in it
as soon as it was dark

I've been here a year now
and much has been gained
from living on my own
completely self-contained.

MY PHILOSOPHY IN A NUTSHELL

nothing to hear

nothing to see

when will the nutcracker

set me free?

THE NUTCRACKER

I'm a nutcracker
no ifs or buts
My job is simple
I crack nuts

The bigger the better
the longer the fatter
The harder they come
the louder they shatter

Walnuts with attitude
the tightest of fits
I squeeze the trigger
and blow them to bits

Brazils take to the hills
pecans grow pale
Nuts shake in their shells
when I'm on their trail

A faceless gunslinger
I ride into town
Cashew! Cashew!
They all fall down.

THE GRANDAD SHOP

I'm going to be a grandad
I'm as happy as can be
Although I must confess
Something's bothering me.

Will I have to visit the grandad shop
and buy some grandad clothes?
A pair of grandad glasses
to perch on the end of my nose?

A grandad woolly cardigan
and a grandad smelly pipe?
Big black boots and a raincoat?
Flat cap, you know the type?

A grandad watch and chain
and a grandad garden shed?
A tobacco-stained moustache
and a grandad baldy head?

A pair of metal bicycle clips
and a grandad rusty bike?
(As my wife is far too young
I'll need a granny lookalike.)

A grandad walking stick
to shake at naughty boys?
A pair of grandad lungs
to make a rattling noise?

I'm going to be a grandad
Can't wait for that first kiss
But think perhaps this grandad
will give the grandad shop a miss.

THE JOURNEY OF A LIFETIME

Are we nearly there yet?
Are we nearly there?

Patience, children, patience,
It's early in the day
The journey has just started
There's still a long, long way.

Are we nearly there yet?
Are we nearly there?

Teenagers, settle down
Relax and don't annoy
There's so much to look at
Why not sit back and enjoy.

Are we nearly there yet?
Are we nearly there?

Grown-ups should know better
I expected more from you
Just round the next bend
The end will be in view.

Are we nearly there yet?
Are we nearly there?

The tank is running on empty
Tyres are worn, the battery low
Headlamps are dim, wipers don't wipe
It's dark and starting to snow.

Are we nearly there yet?
Are we nearly there?

Yes, old friends, you're nearly there
Taken the road as far as it goes
Now the journey of a lifetime
Is drawing to a close.

THE DOLL'S HOUSE

Once upon a not so long ago
a little girl said: 'Build me a doll's house, Daddy.'
'What's the magic word?' said Daddy.
'Please,' said Dorothy.
'That's a good girl,' said Daddy.
And after kissing her goodnight
he turned off the light and went downstairs.

He decided to design and build
the best ever doll's house for his daughter.
It would make her so proud of him.
And so, the very next morning,
he kissed his wife as usual, but instead
of going to work, locked himself in the shed
at the bottom of the garden.

And there he stayed until the days
became weeks and the weeks, months.
At first, he would join the family for meals
but as he explained to his wife
precious time could be saved if she would
be kind enough to leave sandwiches
or a bowl of soup outside his workshop.

After a year, Dorothy's mother begged him,
'If only you would go back to work
we could buy the most expensive doll's house
from the best toy shop in the world.'
'Not good enough for my daughter,' he replied.
'And I'm not coming out until it's finished.'
Then, going back inside, he locked the door.

Years passed.
Sometimes in the middle of the night
Dorothy would creep out of bed,
open the curtains and look out into the garden.
A lamp would be shining in the shed,
and she would see her father silhouetted
against the window like a ghostly shadow puppet.

Years passed.
Dorothy's mother sold the washing machine,
the television, and all the furniture, piece by piece.
She had given up pleading with her husband.
Neither she nor Dorothy saw or spoke to him.
Only heard him hammering and muttering
in his little shed at the bottom of the garden.

Then one morning the door opened
and out stepped an old man, white-haired
and blinking in the sunlight. He called to his wife,
'Tell Dorothy that her doll's house is ready at last.'
But she laughed.'Oh, you stupid man,
your darling daughter is no longer here.'
The old man trembled, 'What do you mean?'

'I mean that she grew up and left school
and got a good job and met a decent man
and left home to marry and settle down.'
Without a word, the old man turned on his heel,
went back into his workshop and locked the door.
Within days, a For Sale sign was posted outside,
the house was sold and the old lady moved away.

* * *

A little girl called Anna is playing in the garden
of her new house. She loves the tangled bushes
and the wooden shed, half-hidden by brambles.
There is no key, but one afternoon her father
manages to force the door open with a chisel.
Spiders, beetles, mice scuttle at the intrusion.
And there on a workbench, covered in cobwebs . . .

It has pride of place in her bedroom now,
a magnificent doll's house with plush carpets
on polished floors. Electricity and running water.
In the kitchen, a fridge and a working oven
In the bathroom a jacuzzi. The little girl
knew that no one had played with it before
and considered herself very lucky indeed.

The only thing she didn't like, and which
she quickly threw away, was a doll she found
in the corner of a bedroom with 'Dorothy'
painted on the door. A shrivelled old man,
hands covering his face like a dreadful mask.
Hunched in sorrow. Inconsolable.

TSUNAMI*

'All in time, all in time, all in time to the music
All in time, all in time, all in time to the music . . .'

The sea is outrageous
It rages and rages
All in time to the music
Manacled to the moon
For ages and ages
All in time to the music

The sea is secretive
Its soul unassailable
All in time to the music
With mountains of water
Black and unscalable
All in time to the music

The sea is stricken
Terribly sick, an'
All in time to the music
Its arteries thicken
Acid and slick, an'
All in time to the music

The sea's in a panic
Unstable and manic
All in time to the music
The earth in its clutches
Everything touches
All in time to the music

When the earth quakes
The devil awakes
All in time to the music
Sends in an army
Satanic tsunami
All in time to the music

What begins as a wave
Becomes a mass grave
All in time to the music
The water recedes
A continent bleeds
All in time to the music.

'All in time, all in time, all in time to the music
All in time, all in time, all in time to the music . . .'

*The spoken chorus begins the poem and continues throughout, providing
an incessant undertow.

INVENTION

I am an invention
Waiting to be invented
Invent me

Champing at the bit
Keyed up and ready to startle
Let me

Clean and plentiful
Cheap and cheerful
A bundle of energy, and free

A cure for all ills
Heart disease? Cancer?
Ghosts of the past, you'll see

Inspiration
Imagination
Communication. All three

I am an invention
Waiting to be invented.
Invent me.

RAINFOREST GATEAU

Too many cooks
Recipe gone wrong
Still on the menu
But not for long.

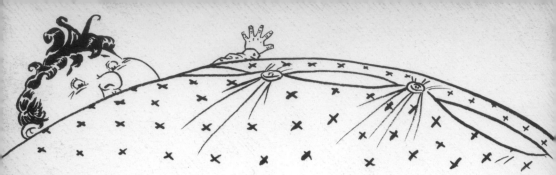

JUST DESSERTS

Jelly and custard, lemon meringue pie
Sherry trifle with cream piled high

Mincemeat tart and blackberry sponge
Roly-poly with syrupy gunge

Chocolate-coated profiterole
Sugary doughnut (without the hole)

Pineapple fritters and crème brûlée
Treacle toffee straight from the tray

Ice cream with banana split in two
Butterscotch fudge, sticky like glue

Rhubarb crumble and strawberry cheesecake
Brandy snaps that'll make your teeth ache

Christmas pudding, just one more slice
For goodness' sake, take my advice:

If all you eat is just desserts
One day you'll get your just desserts.

RECIPES FROM THE

Crazy CAFÉ

COOK BOOK

When not writing poems I
work in my famous restaurant,
the Crazy Café. Customers are
always asking me for the recipes
of their favourite dishes, so here
are just a few.

TOAD IN THE HOLE

Good chefs catch their toads first thing in the morning
while they are fat and fresh (the toads, not the chefs).
But if you are not an early riser you may prefer to use
frozen toads or cans of toads in tomato sauce.
For a nourishing and tasty dish, simply take a large loaf
(white, unsliced), make a hole in the middle,
stuff with the toad mixture and bake in a hot oven
until the cows come home.

RABBIT PIE

From your local butcher buy a large pork pie.
Take it home and carefully remove the crust.
Scrape out all the meat and either throw away
or give to your pet cat/dog/hyena/tiger,
then fill with carrots and lettuce leaves.
Replace the lid and serve immediately.
Rambo, my pet rabbit, loves this pie and I'm sure yours will too.

CUP CAKES

Into a large bowl, pour half a bag of flour,
a glass of water and two teaspoons of sugar.
Using your hands make a lovely mush
and plonk the mixture on to a cold plate,
(Ideally you would use a potter's wheel,
but you may not have one in the kitchen.)
Fashion into the shape of small cups
(there should be enough to make a set of four),
and put into a hot oven to harden.

Cup cakes will come in very useful
when you want to drink tea
and eat cake at the same time.

SURPRISE PUDDING

I adore making puddings that surprise the diners who come
into my café, and here are a few of my favourites:
French fries with custard
Raspberry jelly and kebabs
Apple turnover with bacon and mushy peas
Chocolate mousse and chipolatas
Broccoli-flavoured ice cream with microchip cookies

LEMON SNOW

As soon as it starts to snow, cut your lemons in half,
rush outside and arrange them, cut-side up, on the patio
or along a wall. Next morning, gather them in,
sprinkle with sugar and pop them into the freezer.
Forget all about them until summer comes
and the sun is belting down. Remove from freezer
and enjoy the tangy, refreshing taste of winter.

MISSISSIPPI MUD PIES

They are not as easy to make as they sound
because ordinary mud simply will not do.
Various chefs have experimented using Thames mud,
Mersey mud and even mud from the River Seine,
but none of them seem to work. The secret ingredient that
gives the mud its distinct flavour must have something to do
with the crocodiles who live on the banks of the Mississippi.
So if you have a friend visiting the southern states of the USA
ask if they would fill a few bin liners and bring them back.
Simply strain the mud to get rid of weeds, mosquitoes
and baby crocs, then add sugar, cocoa powder
and, using a spade, fill your buckets and allow to set. Yummy!

BUTTERFLY CAKES

For these delicious cakes you will need a pound of butter
and two and a half cupfuls of flies. Or bluebottles if in season.
Whisk together in a large bowl adding flour and sugar to taste.
For added zing you may wish to throw in a handful
of wasps or bumblebees into the cake mix.
Some chefs mistakenly believe that butterfly cakes
are made out of butterflies. How silly can you get?

CHEESY HEDGEHOGS

To make this popular party treat, abandon a baby
pineapple outside the home of a family of hedgehogs.
Soon the mummy hedgehog, feeling sorry for the poor thing,
will take him inside and feed him. Once fully grown
the pineapple will be thrown out to fend for itself.
Now is the time to rescue it, cut it in half
and serve with cubes of cheese on cocktail sticks.

(A WORD OF WARNING:
DON'T LET THE YOUNGER GUESTS SWALLOW THE COCKTAIL STICKS,
AND DON'T MENTION WHERE THE PINEAPPLE SPENT THE WINTER,
AS THIS MIGHT UPSET THE GROWN-UPS.)

THE RHYMING DINER

Dear Waiter,

I'm sorry but the service was poor.
I'm not being picky
But the cutlery was sticky
And the soup ended up on the floor.

The stew was too gooey
The chicken too chewy
And yuck! that frozen chip.

So enough's enough
I'm off in a huff
Here's a poem instead of a tip.

WISTFUL HAIKU

my biggest regret

is that my books weren't around

when I was at school

INDEX OF FIRST LINES